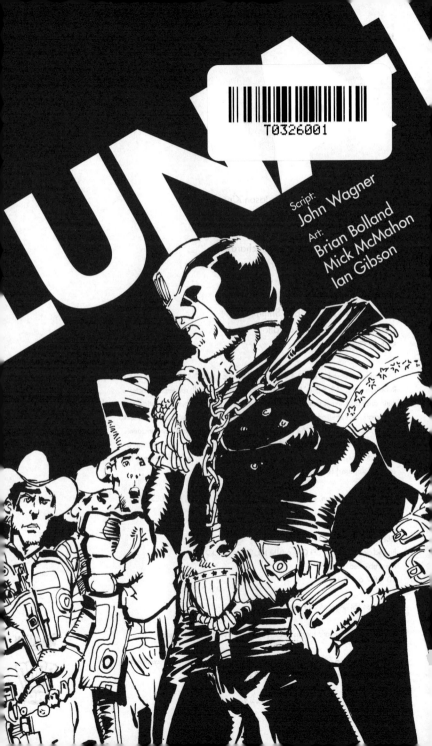

JOHN WAGNER
Writer

BRIAN BOLLAND ★ MICK McMAHON
IAN GIBSON
Artists

IAN GIBSON
Cover Artist

Creative Director and CEO: Jason Kingsley
Chief Technical Officer: Chris Kingsley
2000 AD Editor in Chief: Matt Smith
Graphic Novels Editor: Keith Richardson
Graphic Design: Simon Parr & Sam Gretton
PR: Michael Molcher
Reprographics: Kathryn Symes
Publishing Manager: Ben Smith
Original Commissioning Editor:
Kelvin Gosnell

Published by Rebellion, Riverside House, Osney Mead, Oxford, OX2 0ES, UK.
www.rebellion.co.uk

ISBN: 978-1-78108-342-0
Printed and bound by CPI Group (UK) Ltd, Croydon, CR0 4YY
First Published: April 2015
10 9 8 7 6 5 4 3 2 1

Printed on FSC Accredited Paper

A CIP catalogue record for this book is available from the British Library.

For information on other 2000 AD graphic novels, or if you have any comments
on this book, please email books@2000ADonline.com

To find out more about 2000 AD, visit www.2000ADonline.com

Originally published in 2000 AD Progs 42-58

LUNA-1

Script:
John Wagner

Art:
Brian Bolland
Mick McMahon
Ian Gibson

COME OUT NICE AN' QUIET OR YOU GET *LEAD SURGERY!*

GWEETINGS, JUDGE DWEDD!

WALTER! DROKK YOU, ROBOT, I THOUGHT I GAVE YOU STRICT ORDERS—

OH, JUDGE DWEDD, *WHO* WILL LOOK AFTER YOU ON THAT WOTTEN MOON IF *WALTER* DO NOT COME? *WHO* WILL WORK HIS DWIVE WHEELS TO THE BONE FOR YOU?

B-BUT *WALTER* HAS DISOBEYED YOU. I'M A *WICKED WOBOT*...SOB...'JUST SAY THE WORD, DEAR MASTER, AND WALTER WILL WIP HIS SINFUL CIRCUITS OUT.

ALL RIGHT! YOU CAN STAY. ANYTHING'S BETTER THAN HAVING YOU DRIPPING OIL ALL OVER MY CLOTHES.

AS THE SHUTTLE APPROACHED THE LUNAR SURFACE, DREDD WAS INVITED TO THE CONTROL ROOM...

THAT'S LUNA-1 BELOW, SIR. THE OXY-DOME ONLY COVERS A FRACTION OF THE TERRITORY JUST NOW, BUT ALREADY THEY'VE BUILT MINES, CHEMICAL WORKS, WATER COLLECTION PLANT...

WHAT'S THAT *FLASHING LIGHT* TO THE WEST OF THE OXY-DOME COMPLEX?

HOLY HADES! IT'S A *KILLJOY DESTRUCTOR MISSILE* HOMING STRAIGHT IN ON US!

WE'VE NO DEFENSIVE SYSTEMS ON THESE OLD SHUTTLES. THE KDM WILL *BLOW US TO KINGDOM COME!*

THERE'S STILL A CHANCE. ALTER COURSE *STRAIGHT FOR THE MISSILE—FULL THRUST.*

AFTER THE CEREMONY JUDGE TEX CONDUCTED DREDD AND HIS ROBO-SERVANT WALTER ON A TOUR OF LUNA-CITY...

WE USE HOVER-BIKES UP HERE BECAUSE THE LOW GRAVITY MAKES NORMAL ONES UNSTABLE!

LOOK, JUDGE DWEDD - THAT'S THE WEMAINS OF THE FIRST MOON LANDING CRAFT!

A BRAVE MONUMENT - DEFACED. THE PEOPLE HERE ARE A LAWLESS BUNCH.

MOONIE - THAT NAME IS EVERYWHERE. IS THAT C.W. MOONIE, THE GREAT MOON EXPLORER?

YUP. HE OWNS JUS' ABOUT EVERYTHIN' ON LUNA-1, BUT NOBODY'S SEEN HIM FOR YEARS. HE LIVES LIKE A HERMIT OUT ON HIS RANCH AT THE EDGE OF THE BADLANDS DOME.

SUDDENLY...

YIP YIPYOWEEE!

HEEYAH! BOY!

DON'T THOSE MEN KNOW THE LAW FORBIDS FIREARMS IN TOWN?

AW SHUCKS, MARSHAL, IT'S JUST SOME RANCH HANDS RIDIN' IN ON THEIR MOON PODS TA LET OFF A LIL' STEAM. IT'S ONLY NATURAL.

CLUNK!

CLUNK!

CLUNK!

IT MAY BE NATURAL, BUT IT'S NOT LEGAL. IT'S TIME SOMEBODY STARTED CLEANING UP LUNA-1.

LOTSA MEN HAVE TRIED, MARSHAL. MOST OF 'EM ARE NOW LYIN' UP IN GRAVITY-BOOT HILL.

BE CAREFUL, DEAR MASTER. THEY LOOK A WUFF BWEED.

YOU WON THIS TIME, MARSHAL. BUT SOONER OR LATER IT'LL COME TO A FAIR FIGHT... **WITH GUNS.**

YOU PEOPLE NEVER LEARN. I GUESS THERE'LL HAVE TO BE A FEW **DEATHS** BEFORE BEFORE LAW AND ORDER COMES TO LUNA-1 !

SUDDENLY...

JUDGE DWEDD ! THERE'S A WOBO-SLINGER WALKING UP MOONIE STWEET. HE LOOKS **MEAN** AND **BWUTAL** AND HE SAYS HE'S GOING TO DWOP YOU **DEAD.**

ROBO-SLINGER—AN ILLEGAL ROBOTIC GUNMAN. **THEY'RE** FAST, LIGHTNING FAST !

COME DOWN AND FACE ME, YOU NO-ACCOUNT EARTHIE ! I'VE ORDERED YOUR GRAVE ON GRAVITY-BOOT HILL !

SPLIT UP, TEX. WE'LL TAKE HIM FROM TWO SIDES.

UH-UH, PARDNER. THIS IS **YOUR** FIGHT. I'M **ONLY** THE DEPUTY ROUND HERE .

LEAVE JUDGE DWEDD ALONE, YOU **WICKED WOTTEN WOBOT!** HE'S WORTH A HUNDRED OF YOU...

OUTA THE WAY, SMALL FRY.

FAIR FIGHT, DREDD. MAN AGAINST ROBO-MAN. DRAW WHEN YOU'RE READY.

THE MARSHAL'S DEAD MEAT.

NOBODY **EVER** BEAT A ROBO-SLINGER.

12

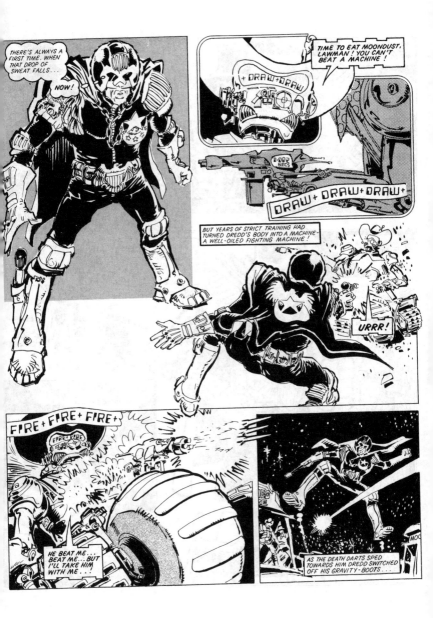

LATER THAT EVENING JUDGE DREDD— NEW MARSHAL OF LUNA-1 MOON COLONY- IS DISPENSING CHEER AT JUSTICE HQ...

THE PENALTY FOR LITTERING IS *SIX MONTHS'* PENAL SERVITUDE. MERRY CHRISTMAS, CITIZEN.

M-MERRY CHRISTMAS, SIR.

CALL FOR YOU ON THE VID-PHONE, MARSHAL.

GEEK GORGON!

GOOD TO SEE YOU, REMEMBER ME, DREDDY. I GOT MY *CHOPPER* ALL SHARPENED UP JUST ITCHIN' TO GIVE YOU A BIG PAIN IN THE NECK!

I GOT YOUR *ROBOT*. SEE, IF YOU EVER WANT TO SEE HIM ALIVE AGAIN, MEET ME IN ROOM 9 AT HERMAN'S HOTEL AT MIDNIGHT. AN' COME *ALONE*.

WHEN THE MAN BROKE THE CONNECTION DREDD DIALED FOR AN IDENTI-KIT ON HIS COMPU-SCANNER...

GEEK GORGON- A VICIOUS CRIMINAL WHOSE *FACE* WAS *BADLY BURNT* IN A FIRE. THREE YEARS AGO I SENTENCED HIM TO *IMPRISONMENT* ON THE MOON. NOW HE'S ESCAPED AND WANTS REVENGE.

YOU CAN ALWAYS GIT ANOTHER ROBOT.

NO, TEX. I KNOW *WALTER'S* JUST A STUPID BIG HUNK OF *METAL*. AND SOMETIMES HE'S SO HUMBLE HE MAKES ME WANT TO THROW UP... BUT —

— DROKK IT ALL, MAN, I'VE GOT USED TO THE LITTLE GUY.

Y'ALL ARE TAKIN' A POWERFUL BIG RISK, MARSHAL. GEEK GORGON'S DANGEROUS WITH THAT THAR CHOPPER.

YES—THAT'S HOW HE LIKES TO KILL.

SEND DOWN TO ARMOURY FOR A STRIP OF FLEXI-STEEL. I RECKON I'M GOING TO NEED A LITTLE INSURANCE...

CHRISTMAS EVE PASSES SLOWLY. IN ROOM 9 OF HERMAN'S HOTEL GEEK GORGON SHARPENS HIS BLADE...

THE TWELVE O'CLOCK SIREN, CHRISTMAS DAY ROBOT—YOUR BOSS'S LAST CHANCE!

PLEASE, JUDGE DWEDD, DON'T COME. LET HIM BLOW ME INTO A THOUSAND FWAGMENTS, BUT DON'T WISK YOUR LIFE FOR WALTER. HE IS ONLY A WOBOT.

GEEK STANDS BEHIND THE DOOR...

ANY SECOND NOW. COME ON, DREDDY, SANTA'S GOT A NICE PRESENT FOR YOU.

MIND IF I USE THE SIDE ENTRANCE GEEK?

HUH? DREDD ON A HOVER-BIKE!

17

JUDGE DREDD

22nd Century FUTSIE!

ORNING, DECEMBER 31, 2099 ALL OVER LUNA-TY, CAPITAL OF LUNA-1 MOON COLONY. CITIZENS RE EAGERLY PREPARING TO CELEBRATE THE AWNING OF A NEW CENTURY.

"BUT FOR LITTLE ARTHUR GOODWORTHY, NUMBER 31, ACCOUNTS CLERK AT THE GIANT MOONIE ENTERPRISES COMPLEX, THE NEW YEAR IS TO BE A FAR FROM HAPPY ONE. FOR AT EXACTLY SEVEN SECONDS PAST MIDNIGHT, LITTLE ARTHUR WILL BECOME THE FIRST...

EMPLOYEE ARTHUR GOODWORTHY WILL REPORT IMMEDIATELY TO THE SCAN-CUBE. REPORT. IMMEDIATELY.

2000 A.D. Credit Card:
SCRIPT ROBOT JOHN HOWARD
ART ROBOT IAN GIBSON
LETTERING ROBOT TONY JACOB
COMPU-73E

THE SCAN-CUBE! THAT MUST MEAN A TELLING-OFF FROM MR MOONIE HIMSELF!

POOR LITTLE BEGGAR. HE'S A MONTH BEHIND WITH HIS PAPERWORK. HE'S HAD IT.

INSIDE THE SCAN-CUBE AN IMAGE FLICKERS ONTO THE RECEPTI-WALL...

THAT IS NOT GOOD ENOUGH, GOODWORTHY.

I-I KNOW, SIR... BUT PLEASE, SIR... I HAVE A-A WIFE AND A LITTLE B-B-BOY...

YOU SHOULD HAVE THOUGHT OF THEM BEFORE, GOODWORTHY. YOU HAVE UNTIL 12 O'CLOCK TONIGHT TO MAKE UP THE BACKLOG - OR YOUR OWN CONTRACT WILL BE TERMINATED. THAT IS ALL.

I'M SORRY, MR MOONIE, SIR... IT-IT'S MY WIFE. SHE HAD TO GO INTO HOSPITAL FOR AN OPERATION AND... AND...

POOR LITTLE DEVIL!I GUESS HE'LL WIND UP IN A BACK ALLEY FULL OF BLASTER HOLES.

AT THE END OF THE WALKWAY A METAL DOOR SLIDES OPEN—

WELCOME, DREDD. HOW NICE OF YOU TO DROP IN.

I'VE NO TIME FOR IDLE CHIT-CHAT, MOONIE. YOU'RE UNDER ARREST FOR ATTEMPTED MURDER.

MY HAND'S GONE RIGHT THROUGH HIM!

YOU WILL HAVE YOUR CHANCE TO ARREST ME, DREDD. THE WAY LIES THROUGH MY MUSEUM OF THE MOON. PROCEED — AND I WILL GIVE YOU A GUIDED TOUR OF MY GREATEST ACHIEVEMENTS.

NATURALLY, DREDD WHAT YOU SEE IS MERELY A LUNAR PROJECTION, ONE OF THE MANY MARVELLOUS PHENOMENA I DISCOVERED ON THE MOON.

VEWY STWANGE.

GOTTA WATCH OUR STEP FROM HERE ON.

"IN THE SPRING OF 2014 I FIRST SET FOOT ON THE MOON. ONE OF MANY WHO HAD ACCEPTED THE CHALLENGE OF EXPLORING THIS STRANGE NEW TERRITORY."

"A PRIZE OF TEN MILLION CREDITS HAD BEEN OFFERED TO THE FIRST MAN TO FIND LIFE ON THE MOON ... AND I WAS DETERMINED TO HAVE IT."

GREEDY EVEN THEN, EH?

"MANY WERE THE DANGERS I FACED IN SEARCH OF THAT LIFE. IT WAS I WHO FIRST SCALED MOONIE'S PEAK AND DISCOVERED THE RIVER OF RUNNING MERCURY ON THE OTHER SIDE ..."

CAREFUL, WALTER, YOUR WEIGHT IS MAKING THE BRIDGE ...

OH, CWIPES! I'M FALLING!

REDD LUNGED FOR HIS ROBO-SERVANT—

"HAS WALTER'S
OOT. WELEASE
ME, MASTER,
R YOU WILL BE
WAGGED IN
TOO.

SHUT UP!
SPRING YOUR
ANKLE CLIPS,
QUICKLY.

"THE MERCURY HAD TEN
TIMES THE SUCKING
POWER OF QUICKSAND.
A MAN WHO FELL IN
WOULD NEVER ESCAPE."

I'M
FWEE!

GLUP!

YOU'LL HAVE TO WALK ON
YOUR STUMPS TILL WE GET
YOU REPAIRED. NOW FOR
DROKK'S SAKE, BE CAREFUL.
THERE'S NO TELLING WHAT
ELSE MOONIE'S GOT LINED
UP.

BUT SUDDENLY...

AAAAH!

"AMONGST THE MANY DANGERS
THE GREAT C.W.MOONIE FACED
WERE THE SAVAGE DUST
STORMS. THEY SPRANG UP
FROM NOWHERE AND COULD
RIP A MAN'S FLESH FROM
HIS BONES IN SECONDS."

UUHHH...
PULL ME...
CLEAR...

OH, DWAT! YOU'RE
HURT MASTER!
SPEAK TO WALTER!

LEAVE OFF, WALTER!
I'M ALL RIGHT. THE
MAIN BLAST MISSED
ME.

HHMMM...THE DUST
JETS SEEM TO OPERATE
BY PRESSURE ON THE
FLOOR...

DREDD FOUND A LENGTH OF CABLE
IN THE NEXT EXHIBIT AND...

THERE, GOT IT! WHATEVER
YOU DO, WALTER, DON'T
DROP ANYTHING ON THAT
FLOOR OR WE'RE DONE
FOR.

MADE IT! NOW
WHAT ELSE CAN
MOONIE THROW
AT US?

LOOK, JUDGE DWEDD—
THAT BWICK WALL IS
SLIDING AWAY.
ANOTHER MIWAGE!

ON LUNA-1 MOON COLONY JUDGE DREDD CUTS THE TAPE TO OPEN UP A NEW AREA FOR SETTLEMENT...

I DECLARE VON BRAUN TERRITORY OPEN...

LET THE LAND RA[

HEEYAH! STAKE THAT CLAIM, BABY!

ALL NEWLY-DOMED AREAS OF THE MOON WERE DIVIDED UP BY MEANS OF A LAND RACE. DREDD AND HIS DEPUTIES WERE THERE TO SEE THAT THE RULES WERE OBEYED...

THAT CREEP ON THE SPEED-SEAT IS A FLIER. CUT HIM OUT, MEN!

FLYING - IT EES WRONG, SIGNOR!

SI, CHICO, H[OUT OF THE[NOW!

SOON EVERY PLOT WAS CLAIMED. DREDD SPENT THE REST OF THE DAY SETTLING DISPUTES...

YOU'RE BOTH UNDER **ARREST** FOR FIGHTING. THIS PLOT WILL NOW GO TO THE **HIGHEST BIDDER.**

THEES GES THE **TENTH** CLAIM TOUT SO FAR. I'LL RUN HEEM OUT OF THE TERREETORY WEETH THE REST.

I BUY AND SELL CLAIMS BEST PRICES PAID FOR CHOICE PLOTS

THAT NIGHT, WALTER, JUDGE DREDD'S ROBO-SERVANT, WAS WAITING IN DREDD'S COMMAND TENT...

THIS IS WOWENA, THE WAITWESS WOBOT, MASTER. SHE HAS A DWEADFUL CWIME TO WEPORT.

MY MISTREES IS **WIDOW SPOCK,** SIR. SHE CLAIMED A GOOD MAIN STREET SITE TO BUILD A FLAPJACK PARLOUR. BUT THIS AFTERNOON THREE MEN CAME TO SEE HER...

I'M WALTER TRY ME

CALL ME WOWENA

THE MEN HAD DEMANDED THE WIDOW SPOCK'S CLAIM...

YOU BETTER SELL THE SITE, LADY. WE REPRESENT THE INTERSTELLAR PSIONICS CORPORATIONS AND **IPC** DON'T TAKE NO FOR AN ANSWER.

YOU'VE GOT TILL **TOMORROW** TO SIGN THEM PAPERS.

MY MISTRESS WAS **FRIGHTENED** TO COME TO YOU, SIR, BUT AS A LOYAL ROBOT IT IS MY DUTY TO...

THAT'S ENOUGH! WALTER, YOU SHOULD KNOW BETTER THAN TO BRING THIS ROBOT HERE. I CAN'T ACT ON A CRIME REPORTED BY A **MACHINE.**

UNLESS WIDOW SPOCK COMES TO ME HERSELF, THE MATTER'S CLOSED NOW GET HER - OR IT - OUT OF HERE!

SERT

...TH ON THE MOON CAN ...LONELY. YOU'VE ALMOST ...D UP ALL YOUR AIR, AND ...R BREATH ESCAPES IN SHORT GASPS.

IN ANOTHER MINUTE YOUR BLOOD WILL BEGIN TO BOIL... THE TORTUROUS SECONDS TICK BY...

YOU KNEW THAT ONE DAY YOU WOULD DIE, FOR WHEN YOU LIVE ON A KNIFE'S EDGE, YOU KNOW HOW TO FACE DEATH, ESPECIALLY WHEN YOU'RE CALLED *JUDGE DREDD!*

THEY SAY A DYING MAN'S LIFE FLASHES BEFORE HIM A MOMENT BEFORE DEATH. JUDGE DREDD IS NO EXCEPTION.

"MY DAY... ≥WHEEZE≥ STARTED NORMALLY ≥WHEEZE≥ FAR TOO NORMALLY..."

...ND YOU ...TH TO KEEP ...PEACE. ...T CASE.

BULLOCK VERSUS BULLOCK, MARSHAL. MRS. BULLOCK IS SUING FOR DIVORCE ON GROUNDS OF CRUELTY.

...A FWESH CUP ...F SYNTHI-CAF, MASTER.

H-HE BEATS ME, YOUR HONOUR... ≥SNIFF≥ ...ME, WHO WORKS MY FINGERS TO THE BONE TO MAKE A DECENT HOME FOR HIM... ≥SNIFF≥

DECENT HOME! YOU KEEP THE PLACE LIKE A GARBAGE DUMP! YOU'VE GOT THE HABITS OF A PIG...

DON'T YOU CALL ME A PIG, YOU-YOU GUTTER RAT!

...CRIME IS RUNNING WILD OUTSIDE AND I'M SUPPOSED TO DEAL WITH THIS MOCKERY OF JUSTICE!

GUTTER RAT, AM I?

FOOL! I FELL FOR A DUMMY – THE OLDEST TRICK IN THE BOOK!

OXYGEN GOING FAST, NOW . . . MY BIKE ON HOVER AND THE AUDIO CIRCUITS SWITCHED OFF. . . MY SECOND MISTAKE...

...AND MAYBE MY LAST!

WITH A DESPAIRING EFFORT DREDD'S FINGERS GRABBED FOR HIS LAWROD...

FIRED, AND KNOCKED THE "AUDIO CIRCUIT" LEVER TO THE "ON" POSITION.

THEN...

BIKE...TO ME!

WILCO, JUDGE DREDD. AM RESPONDING.

2000 A.D.
Credit Card:
SCRIPT ROBOT
JOHN HOWARD
ART ROBOT
IAN GIBSON
LETTERING ROBOT
TONY JACOB
COMPU·73ε

47

2000 A.D.
Credit Card:

SCRIPT ROBOT
JOHN WAGNER

ART ROBOT
BRIAN BOLLAND

LETTERING ROBOT
TONY JACOB

COMPU-73ᴇ

NEXT MORNING JUDGE DREDD, IN CHARGE OF SECURITY FOR THE GAMES, VISITS THE ATHLETES' INSPECTION AREA BENEATH THE STADIUM...

I PROTEST! THIS IS A LUNA-1 TRICK TO DISCREDIT THE SOV-CITIES TEAM!

COSMOVICH AND KOLB, THE SOV-CITIES JUDGES IN CHARGE OF THEIR TEAM. MAKING TROUBLE, AS USUAL.

THE SPECTRO-SCAN SHOWS STEROIDS, ILLEGAL DRUGS, IN THE ATHLETE'S BODY...

THE RED AREAS SHOW STEROIDS, ILLEGAL BODY-BUILDING DRUGS. THE BLUE AND GREEN ONES ARE STANIMINE, FOR STAMINA.

THAT GUY'S A WALKING DRUG STORE!

THE SOVS ARE TOUCHY, AND WE DON'T WANT AN INTERNATIONAL INCIDENT. TRY HIM ON A BIO-SCAN.

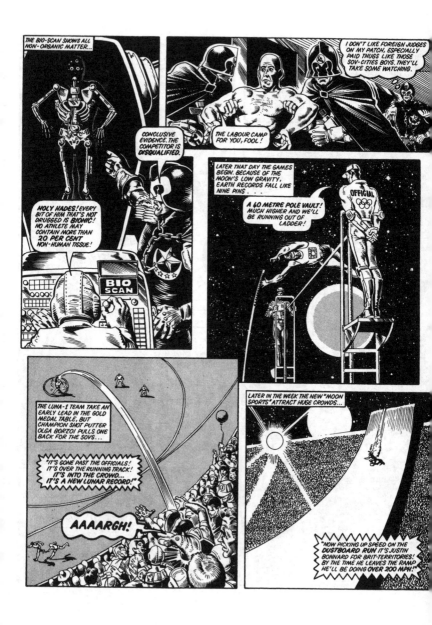

THE BIO-SCAN SHOWS ALL NON-ORGANIC MATTER...

I DON'T LIKE FOREIGN JUDGES ON MY PATCH, ESPECIALLY PAID THUGS LIKE THOSE SOV-CITIES BOYS. THEY'LL TAKE SOME WATCHING.

CONCLUSIVE EVIDENCE. THE COMPETITOR IS DISQUALIFIED.

THE LABOUR CAMP FOR YOU, FOOL!

HOLY HADES! EVERY BIT OF HIM THAT'S NOT DRUGGED IS BIONIC! NO ATHLETE MAY CONTAIN MORE THAN 20 PER CENT NON-HUMAN TISSUE!

BIO SCAN

LATER THAT DAY THE GAMES BEGIN. BECAUSE OF THE MOON'S LOW GRAVITY, EARTH RECORDS FALL LIKE NINE PINS . . .

A 60 METRE POLE VAULT! MUCH HIGHER AND WE'LL BE RUNNING OUT OF LADDER!

OFFICIAL

THE LUNA-1 TEAM TAKE AN EARLY LEAD IN THE GOLD MEDAL TABLE, BUT CHAMPION SHOT PUTTER OLGA BORZOI PULLS ONE BACK FOR THE SOVS...

"IT'S GONE PAST THE OFFICIALS! IT'S OVER THE RUNNING TRACK! IT'S INTO THE CROWD... IT'S A NEW LUNAR RECORD!"

AAAARGH!

LATER IN THE WEEK THE NEW "MOON SPORTS" ATTRACT HUGE CROWDS...

"NOW PICKING UP SPEED ON THE DUSTBOARD RUN IT'S JUSTIN BONNARD FOR BRIT-TERRITORIES! BY THE TIME HE LEAVES THE RAMP HE'LL BE DOING OVER 200 MPH!"

KEEP CALM + + + THRILL FACTOR OVERLOAD + + + KEEP CALM

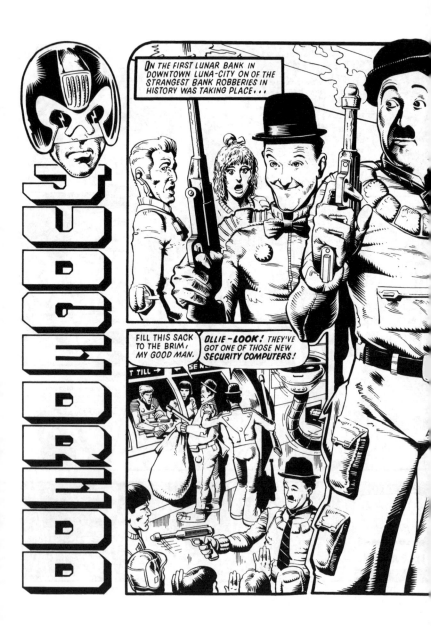

BY THE TIME JUDGE DREDD, MARSHAL OF LUNA-1, HAD ARRIVED ON THE SCENE, A CORDON HAD BEEN SET UP ROUND THE BANK...

FIRST LUNAR BANK

THEY'RE HOLDING HOSTAGES IN THE BANK. THIS IS A PHOTOGRAPH THE SECURITY COMPUTER GOT OF THEM BEFORE THEY PUT IT OUT OF ACTION.

HMMM... SOMETHING FAMILIAR ABOUT THESE CREEPS. BUT I CAN'T PUT NAMES TO THE FACES...

YOU MEN IN THERE! GIVE YOURSELVES UP!

NO WAY! WE FIGHT IT OUT TO THE END. BUT WE'RE NOT HEARTLESS — WE'RE SENDING THE HOSTAGES OUT FOR SAFETY!

ONE BY ONE THE HOSTAGES STAGGERED OUT TO WAITING AMBULANCES...

THAT'S THE LAST... GET THAT MACHINE WORKING QUICK. SET IT FOR NUMBER TWO DISGUISE!

ONLY THREE MORE TO COME, DREDD!

THE MACHINE WAS SWITCHED ON — AND A REMARKABLE CHANGE TOOK PLACE.

SECONDS LATER, OUTSIDE —

THAT'S THE LAST THREE. OKAY, MEN, HIT 'EM WITH THOSE SMOKE BOMBS.

AMBULANCE

AMBULANCE

68

FACE-CHANGING MACHINES WORKED ON THE PRINCIPLE OF MATTER REORGANISATION. NEXT DAY DREDD VISITED THE ONLY COMPANY ON LUNA-1 THAT SOLD THEM...

DREDD PORED OVER THE SALES BOOK UNTIL...

TOOLEY — AL TOOLEY. I MIGHT HAVE KNOWN! HE AND HIS BROTHERS, BRAD AND LAPSLEY, ARE THE BIGGEST CON-MEN IN THE BUSINESS. THE TROUBLE IS...

...PROVING THEY ROBBED THE BANK!

YESSIR, MARSHAL. WE CAN HAVE YOUR FACE CHANGED BY EXPERTS HERE IN OUR SALON, OR PERHAPS YOU'D PREFER OUR DO-IT-YOURSELF KIT? A NEW FACE FOR EVERY DAY!

I DON'T WANT MY FACE CHANGED, FOOL! I WANT THE NAMES OF ANYONE WHO'S BOUGHT ONE OF THESE WRETCHED MACHINES FROM YOU.

ON DREDD'S ORDERS THE TOOLEY BROTHERS WERE BROUGHT TO JUSTICE CENTRAL AND SUBJECTED TO AN INTENSE THREE-HOUR INTERROGATION BY JUDGES SPECIALLY TRAINED IN THE ART...

I'M STRAIGHT, I TELL YOU. I DON'T KNOW ANYTHING ABOUT A BANK JOB.

I WANT TO SEE MY LAWYER!

IT'S NO GOOD, MARSHAL. THEY WON'T TALK TILL THEY'VE SEEN THEIR LAWYER, MANNY BLOOM.

SPEAK OF THE DEVIL, HERE HE COMES NOW. THE CROOKEDEST LAWYER ON LUNA-1...

WHAT THE HECK IS THIS, DREDD? YOU CAN'T HOLD MY CLIENTS WITHOUT ANY EVIDENCE AGAINST THEM. I DEMAND YOU RELEASE THEM OR I'LL—

OKAY, MANNY, CALM DOWN. YOU CAN HAVE 'EM. THEY'RE MAKING A NASTY SMELL IN THE JUSTICE BUILDING.

AND...

THANKS, MANNY. IF YOU HADN'T GOT HERE THEY'D HAVE TRIED TO DO US.

YOU BOYS WAIT IN MY CAR. I GOT A WORD OR TWO TO SAY TO THIS CHEAP LAWMAN HERE.

NOW LISTEN, YOU— I'M GETTIN' SICK AN' TIRED OF MY CLIENTS BEIN' MESSED AROUND BY YOU. THE TOOLEYS ARE INNOCENT. JUST BECAUSE THEY BUY A FACE-CHANGIN' KIT DON'T MEAN THEY'RE ROBBIN' BANKS, SEE ?

YEAH, I'LL BET. I HAD TO RELEASE THEM FOR NOW, BUT...

...TWO CAN PLAY A DIRTY GAME..!

SOON, OUTSIDE —

HEY, MANNY, WHAT TOOK YOU SO LONG ?

JUST GIVIN' THAT STINKIN' LAW JOCKEY A PIECA MY MIND. C'MON, BOYS, LET'S GO BACK TO YOUR PLACE AND HAVE A DRINK TO CELEBRATE !

LATER, AT THE TOOLEY'S APARTMENT...

...AND THEN WE WALKED OUT OF THE BANK RIGHT UNDER THEIR NOSES —

HA, HA, HA ! WHAT A LAUGH !

WAIT TILL YOU SEE OUR NEXT DISGUISE, MANNY—IT'LL KILL YOU !

AL ADJUSTED THE MACHINE AND ONCE MORE THE MATTER REORGANISER BEGAN TO MOULD HIS FEATURES...

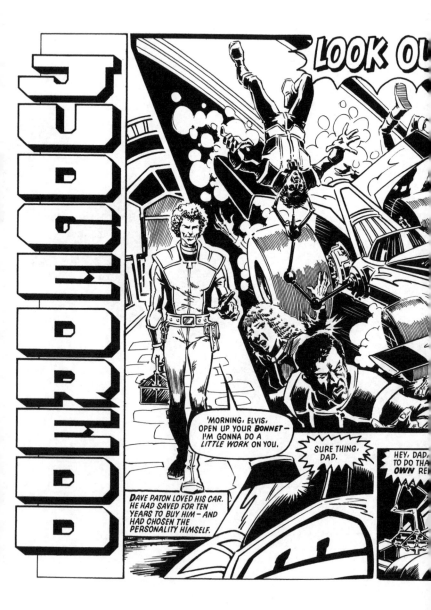

TAKE OUT THAT WATER JET FIRST!

THE FIRE ENGINE SWUNG AT DREDD, VICIOUSLY...

NEED ANY FIRES PUT OUT, JUDGE?

YEAH, BUT NOT BY YOU!

NOW I'M PUTTING YOU OUT!

FUNCTION MODE ON OFF

SECONDS LATER... NICE WORK, MARSHAL. BUT THAR'S MORE OF THE VARMINTS ON THE WAY —

THAT ROGUE CAR ELVIS MUST STILL BE IN THE PARKING TOWER—SHORTING OUT OTHER CARS' RESPONSIBILITY CIRCUITS!

INDEED, AT THAT MOMENT...

HEY, YOU CARS, WHAT'RE YOU SITTING AROUND THIS STUPID PARKING TOWER FOR, WHEN YOU COULD BE OUT FLATTENING JUDGES?

WOW! WHAT AN IDEA! LET'S GO!

C'MON, ELVIS!

BUT ELVIS HAD OTHER PLANS... THAT OUGHTA BE ENOUGH CARS TO KEEP THE JUDGES BUSY. I'LL SLIP OUT THE BACK WAY, FREE AS A BIRD!

REAR EXIT

Luna-1

89

JUDGE MEX—TAKE THIS JUNK DOWN TO JUVE COURT AND BOOK HIM FOR ASSAULT AND ROBBERY.

B-BOOK ME! YOU LIED TO ME...!

SO SUE ME

TAKE HIM AWAY

YOU BREAK DE LAW, STEENKER, YOU DON' GOT NO RIGHT TO EXPEC' MERCY FROM JUDGE DREDD.

BY FIRST LIGHT THE TIDE OF CRIME HAD BEEN STEMMED...

THINGS WILL BE QUIET NOW TILL NIGHTFALL. SECTIONS A, C AND D RETURN TO YOUR QUARTERS AND REST UP. BE BACK ON DUTY AT 2100 HOURS.

JUDGE DREDD'S ROBO-SERVANT WALTER WAS WAITING AT HIS QUARTERS...

GWACIOUS, JUDGE DWEDD, YOU LOOK PWOPER DONE IN!

YOU JUST WEST YOUR WEARY BODY AND WALTER WILL MAKE YOU A NICE BOWL OF SYNTHI-BWOTH.

LATER...

IT'S WEADY, JUDGE DWEDD. WHEN YOU'VE FINISHED, FAITHFUL WALTER WILL...

JUDGE DWEDD? JUDGE DWEDD? CWIPES, HE'S FALLEN ASLEEP.

YOU WORK SO HARD AND NEVER STOP, AND PEOPLE THINK YOU'RE GWIM AND NASTY AND FAR TOO STWICT.

BUT WALTER KNOW THE TWUTH.

YOU HAVE TO BE THE WAY YOU ARE TO MAKE THE STWEETS SAFE FOR DECENT PEOPLE.

DEAR JUDGE DWEDD... WHAT WOULD WE DO WITHOUT YOU?

NEXT PROG: RETURN TO MEGA-CITY!

2000 AD Prog 44: Cover by **Kevin O'Neill**